Give
Hope

A Grieving Journal
to Remember the One You Lost

D1601978

Jen Larsen

Give Hope
A Grieving Journal to Remember the One You Lost
Copyright © 2022 by Jen Larsen

To request permissions, contact the publisher
at freedomhousepublishingco@gmail.com or
Lc.jenlarsen@gmail.com.
Hardback ISBN: 978-1-952566-57-8
Paperback ISBN: 978-1-952566-54-7
Printed in the USA.
Freedom House Publishing Co
Middleton, ID 83644
www.freedomhousepublishingco.com

FREEDOM HOUSE
PUBLISHING CO

hope

[[hohp] noun

the belief that anything is possible, the
only thing stronger than fear,
deep-rooted faith.

#givehope

Give Hope:
A Grieving Journal

To the heartbroken...My heart is with you...

*I hope you find this journal as a source of hope
and light that can give you comfort and healing in your
grieving journey during your darkest hours of life.*

Dear Friend,

At the one year mark of our family's second unexpected death of one of our daughters, I had a vision that I needed to create this journal. I have found solace in journaling after each loss. I have written my most sacred moments of seeing God's hand. I have written of tiny miracles that I have noticed throughout the journey. I have written of my deepest, darkest sorrows and fears. I have allowed my harsh, raw anger to be written onto paper. I have also written of the most beautiful memories of each of my daughters' lives, moments that will live on in my heart. I have documented each milestone I have hit during the first year or years of loss along this road. I have shared my feelings no matter what they might be at the time, with no reservations and no judgment.

Milestones, memories, tender mercies, heartache, gut-wrenching pain, and love.

ALL OF IT!

After the passing of my 2nd daughter, we would honor her by adding #GiveHope to all social media posts in regards to her. All our family, friends and community did the same. Upon finishing this journal, God and my Angel Daughter made it clear that I was supposed to title the journal "Give Hope." I could not have come up with a more perfect title.

I pray this journal allows you to process all of your emotions of loss in this mortal life. I pray that you will see your humanness and know how sacred each and every moment is. God sees you. He sees all of you. He knows you personally. He undoubtedly is in the dark and heaviness of your heart. He is also the source of light that bursts through your heart for the love you feel for your loved one.

This, My Friend, is the beginning to finding healing in the journey and living the legacy for your loved one. May you feel their love for you every time you write. I know that you will have moments of peace in your life now and forever as you document such sacred moments.

I send my love and light to you always.

Your Friend,

Jen

In Honor of my daughters,
Kylie and Kamber

Journaling Sections

I have divided this journal into sections to help organize your experiences through grief. In my own life, I will remember a particular experience I've had and later I want to go back and reference my writings about it. This process will make it easy for you to find those entries.

Each section listed contains some guidance and prompts. You will find a free writing section in "Be Still My Soul" to really pour out your heart onto paper. My hope is that you will find hope and healing in your grief through the process of writing.

Love your friend,

Jen

5 Stages of Grief

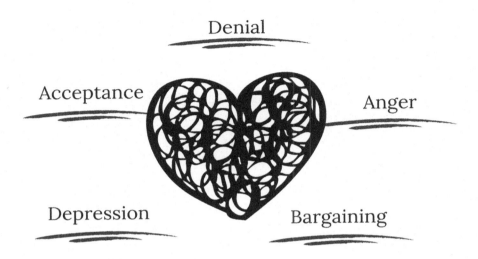

Denial

Acceptance

Anger

Depression

Bargaining

Grief is not linear. We do not move from one stage to another in a line, like robots. Grief is all of the feelings. Oftentimes, how one person deals with grief won't be how each of us deal with it. The grieving process is unique to you. There are no wrong or right ways to feel. All feelings are normal and valid. Grief is messy and you can move through all these stages at different times and do them over and over. I don't think we ever completely heal from grief. I believe we GROW around it, learning how to mold and fit it into our lives. We become stronger and learn so much about ourselves because of it. I believe that until we are with our loved one again, we will always feel their loss and that is OK, because without LOVE there wouldn't be a loss to be felt.

Love your friend,

Jen

Prompts

On days you feel overwhelmed and really don't know where to start, start here. These prompts are to be used as you need them. There are a few prompts already sprinkled throughout the sections. I have also provided plenty of free writing in each category. It will allow you to tailor your journal specifically to you.

Sending you healing wishes on your journey,

Jen

I miss you most when…

My first memory of you is…

The things that trigger my grief the most…

The stage of grief I feel stuck in is…

Today I feel…

I can have Hope in loss by…

What I know about this life now, that I didn't know before is…

My grief feels…

I know angels are present when…

I have seen tiny miracles…

I remember you smelled like…

Your favorite music was…

My favorite thing to do with you was…

I'm ready to feel…

What I know about you now, that I didn't know before is…

Prompts (continued)

Your legacy is…

I will live your legacy by…

My hopes and dreams for the future are…

I feel heaven close when…

Everytime I see _____ I think of you…

This week has been…

The waves of grief feel like…

Your funeral was…

I feel guilty when…

Grief is…

I regret…

My Favorite poem is…

My heart feels like…

I can be kind to myself by…

What can I learn from this…

What I have learned from this…

The hardest part of the day is…

10 words that describe you…

What I wish I could tell you…

How losing you has changed me…

The hardest thing to deal with is…

The quote that makes me think of you…

The signs that make me think of you…

I can still find joy in…

My fears are…

I feel anger when…

I'm grateful for…

Something that triggers my grief is…

Prompts (continued)

The part of my body that holds most of my grief is…

A scripture that helps me is…

When I hear the song, _____, I feel comfort…

What is something you want others to understand when you are really struggling…

What makes me feel most at peace…

What does a joy-filled life look like after loss?

What worries me the most…

When alone, I…

The memory that makes me laugh the most is…

The memory I do not want to remember is…

My support system is…

I feel God when…

I feel the spirit when…

My last adventure with you was…

The day you died…

The last time I was with you…

You made me feel…

I continue to feel you in my life when…

Journaling is like whispering to one's self and listening at the same time.

———— ♡ ♡ ♡ ————

-Mina Murray

Memories

"The Loss is immeasurable.
But so is the LOVE left behind..."

Love leaves a memory, no one can steal. In this section, take your time recording all the beautiful, funny, happy, joyous, sad, hard or painful memories of your loved one, whichever they may be. Know that often they are all of these. Take a moment out of your day to record these precious memories as they come to you. I know that you will feel your loved one near. One day you will be grateful to have this beautiful gift of written memories to look back on. This, my friend, is your first step in having hope in your loss.

Love your friend,

Jen

Memories   **Date:___/___/___.**

My favorite memory with you is_____

_____

_____

_____

_____

_____

_____

_____

_____

_____

                                       Date:___/___/___.

The thing I love about your personality is_____

_____

_____

_____

_____

_____

_____

_____

_____

_____

_____

Memories

Memories   **Date:___/___/___.**

I don't want to ever forget_____

_____

_____

_____

_____

_____

_____

_____

_____

_____

_____

                                                Date:___/___/___.

Your most beautiful trait is _____

_____

_____

_____

_____

_____

_____

_____

_____

_____

_____

_____

_____

Memories

_____
_____
_____
_____
_____
_____
_____
_____
_____
_____
_____
_____
_____
_____
_____
_____
_____
_____
_____
_____
_____
_____
_____
_____

Memories

My 3 favorite qualities about you are _____

_____

_____

_____

_____

_____

_____

_____

_____

_____

Date:___/___/___.

You would always say_____

_____

_____

_____

_____

_____

_____

_____

_____

_____

_____

12 || *Jen Larsen*

Memories

_____

_____

_____

_____

_____

_____

_____

_____

_____

_____

_____

_____

_____

_____

_____

_____

_____

_____

_____

_____

_____

_____

_____

_____

_____

_____

Memories   **Date:___/___/___.**

Your favorite things are _____

_____

_____

_____

_____

_____

_____

_____

_____

_____

                                                Date:___/___/___.

The memory that makes me laugh the most is _____

_____

_____

_____

_____

_____

_____

_____

_____

_____

_____

_____

_____

Memories

_____
_____
_____
_____
_____
_____
_____
_____
_____
_____
_____
_____
_____
_____
_____
_____
_____
_____
_____
_____
_____
_____
_____
_____
_____
_____
_____
_____

Memories

_____
_____
_____
_____
_____
_____
_____
_____
_____
_____
_____
_____
_____
_____
_____
_____
_____
_____
_____
_____
_____
_____
_____
_____
_____
_____
_____
_____
_____

Memories

Memories

_____
_____
_____
_____
_____
_____
_____
_____
_____
_____
_____
_____
_____
_____
_____
_____
_____
_____
_____
_____
_____
_____
_____
_____
_____
_____
_____
_____
_____

Memories

Memories

Memories

Date:___/___/___.

Memories   **Date:___/___/___.**

_____

_____

_____

_____

_____

_____

_____

_____

_____

_____

_____

_____

_____

_____

_____

_____

_____

_____

_____

_____

_____

_____

_____

_____

_____

_____

_____

_____

Memories

_____

_____

_____

_____

_____

_____

_____

_____

_____

_____

_____

_____

_____

_____

_____

_____

_____

_____

_____

_____

_____

_____

_____

_____

_____

Memories   **Date:**___ / ___ / ___ .

_____

_____

_____

_____

_____

_____

_____

_____

_____

_____

_____

_____

_____

_____

_____

_____

_____

_____

_____

_____

_____

_____

_____

_____

_____

_____

_____

Memories

_____
_____
_____
_____
_____
_____
_____
_____
_____
_____
_____
_____
_____
_____
_____
_____
_____
_____
_____
_____
_____
_____
_____
_____

Memories

Date:___/___/___.

_____
_____
_____
_____
_____
_____
_____
_____
_____
_____
_____
_____
_____
_____
_____
_____
_____
_____
_____
_____
_____
_____
_____
_____
_____

Memories   Date:___/___/___.

_____
_____
_____
_____
_____
_____
_____
_____
_____
_____
_____
_____
_____
_____
_____
_____
_____
_____
_____
_____
_____
_____
_____
_____
_____
_____
_____

Memories

Memories

Memories

Date:___ / ___ / ___ .

Memories

_____

_____

_____

_____

_____

_____

_____

_____

_____

_____

_____

_____

_____

_____

_____

_____

_____

_____

_____

_____

_____

_____

_____

_____

_____

_____

_____

Memories

Date:___/___/___.

Memories

_____
_____
_____
_____
_____
_____
_____
_____
_____
_____
_____
_____
_____
_____
_____
_____
_____
_____
_____
_____
_____
_____
_____
_____
_____
_____

Memories

Memories

There are some who bring
a light
so great to the world
that even after they have gone
the light remains.

———————— ♡ ♡ ♡ ————————

Tender Mercies

*"The tender mercies of the Lord are real and they do
not occur randomly or merely by coincidence."*
~David A. Bednar

The tender mercies in life are moments when you see and feel the spiritual influence in your life. It is when you have no doubt that your loved one is near. It is a service given to you by loving people that shows you God is aware of you. It's a sign of God's hand working in your life. They are tiny, little miracles that show up in your day and often when you least expect it. These are some of the most tender and healing moments ever given to us in this life. As you go throughout your days, notice the miracles and write these beautiful experiences down so you can always remember the way you felt.

Love your friend,

Jen

Tender Mercies   **Date:___/___/___.**

Acts of Kindness given_____

_____

_____

_____

_____

_____

_____

_____

_____

_____

_____

_____

_____

_____

_____

_____

_____

_____

_____

_____

_____

_____

_____

_____

_____

_____

Tender Mercies

Acts of Kindness given_____

_____

_____

_____

_____

_____

_____

_____

_____

_____

_____

_____

_____

_____

_____

_____

_____

_____

_____

_____

_____

_____

_____

_____

_____

_____

_____

Tender Mercies   **Date:___/___/___.**

I feel you near when _____

_____

_____

_____

_____

_____

_____

_____

_____

_____

_____

                                      Date:___/___/___.

My miracle today is_____

_____

_____

_____

_____

_____

_____

_____

_____

_____

_____

Tender Mercies

_____
_____
_____
_____
_____
_____
_____
_____
_____
_____
_____
_____
_____
_____
_____
_____
_____
_____
_____
_____
_____
_____
_____
_____
_____
_____

Tender Mercies   **Date:___/___/___.**

I feel heaven when_____

_____

_____

_____

_____

_____

_____

_____

_____

_____

_____

                                      Date:___/___/___.

I know without a doubt that_____

_____

_____

_____

_____

_____

_____

_____

_____

_____

Tender Mercies

_____
_____
_____
_____
_____
_____
_____
_____
_____
_____
_____
_____
_____
_____
_____
_____
_____
_____
_____
_____
_____
_____
_____
_____
_____
_____
_____

Tender Mercies   **Date:___/___/___.**

I have faith in_____

_____

_____

_____

_____

_____

_____

_____

_____

_____

_____

                                                      Date:___/___/___.

An answer to my prayers is_____

_____

_____

_____

_____

_____

_____

_____

_____

_____

_____

Tender Mercies

Tender Mercies   Date:____/____/____.

_____

_____

_____

_____

_____

_____

_____

_____

_____

_____

_____

_____

_____

_____

_____

_____

_____

_____

_____

_____

_____

_____

_____

_____

_____

_____

_____

_____

Tender Mercies

_____

_____

_____

_____

_____

_____

_____

_____

_____

_____

_____

_____

_____

_____

_____

_____

_____

_____

_____

_____

_____

_____

_____

_____

_____

Tender Mercies   Date:____/____/____.

_____
_____
_____
_____
_____
_____
_____
_____
_____
_____
_____
_____
_____
_____
_____
_____
_____
_____
_____
_____
_____
_____
_____
_____
_____
_____

Tender Mercies   Date:____/____/____.

_____

_____

_____

_____

_____

_____

_____

_____

_____

_____

_____

_____

_____

_____

_____

_____

_____

_____

_____

_____

_____

_____

_____

_____

Tender Mercies

_____

_____

_____

_____

_____

_____

_____

_____

_____

_____

_____

_____

_____

_____

_____

_____

_____

_____

_____

_____

_____

_____

_____

_____

_____

_____

_____

_____

_____

Tender Mercies

_____
_____
_____
_____
_____
_____
_____
_____
_____
_____
_____
_____
_____
_____
_____
_____
_____
_____
_____
_____
_____
_____
_____
_____
_____

Tender Mercies

Tender Mercies

_____

_____

_____

_____

_____

_____

_____

_____

_____

_____

_____

_____

_____

_____

_____

_____

_____

_____

_____

_____

_____

_____

_____

_____

_____

Tender Mercies   Date:___/___/___.

_____
_____
_____
_____
_____
_____
_____
_____
_____
_____
_____
_____
_____
_____
_____
_____
_____
_____
_____
_____
_____
_____
_____
_____
_____
_____
_____
_____

Tender Mercies

_____

_____

_____

_____

_____

_____

_____

_____

_____

_____

_____

_____

_____

_____

_____

_____

_____

_____

_____

_____

_____

_____

_____

_____

_____

_____

_____

_____

Tender Mercies   **Date:___/___/___.**

Tender Mercies   **Date:** ___ / ___ / ___ .

_____
_____
_____
_____
_____
_____
_____
_____
_____
_____
_____
_____
_____
_____
_____
_____
_____
_____
_____
_____
_____
_____
_____
_____
_____
_____
_____
_____
_____
_____

Tender Mercies   **Date:___/___/___.**

_____

_____

_____

_____

_____

_____

_____

_____

_____

_____

_____

_____

_____

_____

_____

_____

_____

_____

_____

_____

_____

_____

_____

_____

_____

_____

_____

_____

_____

_____

Tender Mercies   **Date:___/___/___.**

_____

_____

_____

_____

_____

_____

_____

_____

_____

_____

_____

_____

_____

_____

_____

_____

_____

_____

_____

_____

_____

_____

_____

_____

_____

_____

Tender Mercies   **Date:___/___/___.**

_____

_____

_____

_____

_____

_____

_____

_____

_____

_____

_____

_____

_____

_____

_____

_____

_____

_____

_____

_____

_____

_____

_____

_____

_____

_____

Tender Mercies   Date:____/____/____.

_____
_____
_____
_____
_____
_____
_____
_____
_____
_____
_____
_____
_____
_____
_____
_____
_____
_____
_____
_____
_____
_____
_____
_____
_____

Tender Mercies   **Date:___/___/___.**

Tender Mercies

_____
_____
_____
_____
_____
_____
_____
_____
_____
_____
_____
_____
_____
_____
_____
_____
_____
_____
_____
_____
_____
_____
_____
_____

Tender Mercies   **Date:___/___/____.**

_____
_____
_____
_____
_____
_____
_____
_____
_____
_____
_____
_____
_____
_____
_____
_____
_____
_____
_____
_____
_____
_____
_____
_____
_____
_____
_____

Tender Mercies   **Date:___/___/___.**

_____
_____
_____
_____
_____
_____
_____
_____
_____
_____
_____
_____
_____
_____
_____
_____
_____
_____
_____
_____
_____
_____
_____
_____
_____
_____
_____
_____

Tender Mercies   Date:____/____/____.

_____

_____

_____

_____

_____

_____

_____

_____

_____

_____

_____

_____

_____

_____

_____

_____

_____

_____

_____

_____

_____

_____

_____

_____

_____

_____

_____

_____

_____

_____

Tender Mercies   **Date:___/___/___.**

In all of the sadness, when
You're feeling that your
heart is empty, and lacking,
remember that grief isn't
the absence of love.
Grief is the proof that love
is still there.

——————— ♡ ♡ ♡ ———————

– Tessa Schaffer

Milestones

1 year,

12 months,

365 days,

8,760 hours,

525,600 minutes,

3,153,600 seconds,

Every day,

Every night,

Every time,

I always miss you.

During our first year of loss, we endure all our firsts without our loved one. It is such a tender time. I put this section here so you can record these sacred stepping stones in your grief.

Love your friend,

Jen

Milestones

Month 1   Date:___/___/___.

_____
_____
_____
_____
_____
_____
_____
_____
_____
_____
_____
_____
_____
_____
_____
_____
_____
_____
_____
_____
_____
_____
_____
_____
_____
_____
_____

Milestones

Month 2   **Date:___/___/____.**

Milestones

Month 3   **Date:___/___/___.**

_____

_____

_____

_____

_____

_____

_____

_____

_____

_____

_____

_____

_____

_____

_____

_____

_____

_____

_____

_____

_____

_____

_____

_____

_____

_____

_____

_____

_____

_____

Milestones

Month 4   **Date:___/___/___.**

_____

_____

_____

_____

_____

_____

_____

_____

_____

_____

_____

_____

_____

_____

_____

_____

_____

_____

_____

_____

_____

_____

_____

_____

_____

_____

_____

_____

Milestones

Month 5   **Date:**___/___/___.

Milestones

Month 6

Date: ___/___/___.

Milestones

Month 7   Date:___/___/___.

_____

_____

_____

_____

_____

_____

_____

_____

_____

_____

_____

_____

_____

_____

_____

_____

_____

_____

_____

_____

_____

_____

_____

_____

_____

_____

Milestones

Month 8   **Date:___/___/___.**

Milestones

Month 9   **Date:**___/___/___.

Milestones

Month 10   **Date:**___/___/___.

Milestones

Month 11   **Date:___/___/___.**

_____

_____

_____

_____

_____

_____

_____

_____

_____

_____

_____

_____

_____

_____

_____

_____

_____

_____

_____

_____

_____

_____

_____

_____

_____

_____

_____

_____

_____

_____

Milestones

1 Year Mark

Date:___/___/___.

_____

_____

_____

_____

_____

_____

_____

_____

_____

_____

_____

_____

_____

_____

_____

_____

_____

_____

_____

_____

_____

_____

_____

_____

_____

_____

Milestones   Date:____/____/____.

It's your Birthday! Happy Birthday!_____

_____

_____

_____

_____

_____

_____

_____

_____

_____

_____

_____

_____

_____

_____

_____

_____

_____

_____

_____

_____

_____

_____

_____

_____

_____

Holidays:

January   **Date:___/___/___.**

_____
_____
_____
_____
_____
_____
_____
_____
_____
_____
_____

February   **Date:___/___/___.**

_____
_____
_____
_____
_____
_____
_____
_____
_____
_____
_____

Holidays:

March   **Date:___ / ___ / ___.**

_____

_____

_____

_____

_____

_____

_____

_____

_____

April   **Date:___ / ___ / ___.**

_____

_____

_____

_____

_____

_____

_____

_____

_____

_____

_____

_____

Holidays:

May   **Date:___/___/___.**

_____

_____

_____

_____

_____

_____

_____

_____

_____

June   **Date:___/___/___.**

_____

_____

_____

_____

_____

_____

_____

_____

_____

_____

Holidays:

July   **Date:___/___/___.**

_____
_____
_____
_____
_____
_____
_____
_____
_____

August   **Date:___/___/___.**

_____
_____
_____
_____
_____
_____
_____
_____
_____
_____
_____
_____

Holidays:

September   **Date:___/___/___.**

_____

_____

_____

_____

_____

_____

_____

_____

_____

_____

October   **Date:___/___/___.**

_____

_____

_____

_____

_____

_____

_____

_____

_____

_____

_____

Holidays:

November   **Date:___/___/___.**

_____
_____
_____
_____
_____
_____
_____
_____
_____

December   **Date:___/___/___.**

_____
_____
_____
_____
_____
_____
_____
_____
_____
_____
_____
_____

Milestones

Date:____/____/____.

_____
_____
_____
_____
_____
_____
_____
_____
_____
_____
_____
_____
_____
_____
_____
_____
_____
_____
_____
_____
_____
_____
_____
_____
_____
_____
_____
_____
_____

Milestones

Anniversary   Date:___/___/___.

_____
_____
_____
_____
_____
_____
_____
_____

Anniversary   Date:___/___/___.

_____
_____
_____
_____
_____
_____
_____
_____
_____
_____
_____
_____

Milestones

_____
_____
_____
_____
_____
_____
_____
_____
_____
_____
_____
_____
_____
_____
_____
_____
_____
_____
_____
_____
_____
_____
_____
_____
_____
_____

Milestones   Date:___ /___ /___ .

_____

_____

_____

_____

_____

_____

_____

_____

_____

_____

_____

_____

_____

_____

_____

_____

_____

_____

_____

_____

_____

_____

_____

_____

_____

_____

_____

_____

_____

_____

Milestones   Date:___/___/___.

Milestones   Date:___/___/___.

_____
_____
_____
_____
_____
_____
_____
_____
_____
_____
_____
_____
_____
_____
_____
_____
_____
_____
_____
_____
_____
_____
_____
_____
_____
_____
_____
_____

Milestones

_____
_____
_____
_____
_____
_____
_____
_____
_____
_____
_____
_____
_____
_____
_____
_____
_____
_____
_____
_____
_____
_____
_____
_____
_____
_____
_____
_____

Milestones

_____

_____

_____

_____

_____

_____

_____

_____

_____

_____

_____

_____

_____

_____

_____

_____

_____

_____

_____

_____

_____

_____

_____

_____

_____

Milestones

Milestones   Date:___/___/___.

Milestones

Date:___/___/___.

_____
_____
_____
_____
_____
_____
_____
_____
_____
_____
_____
_____
_____
_____
_____
_____
_____
_____
_____
_____
_____
_____
_____
_____
_____
_____
_____
_____
_____

There is a sacredness in tears.
They are not the mark of weakness,
but of power.
They speak more eloquently than
ten thousand tongues.
They are the messengers of
overwhelming grief,
of deep contrition, and
of unspeakable love

——————————— ♡ ♡ ♡ ———————————

-Washington Irving

Heart to Heart

"Love is an invisible thread
that ties two hearts together."

This is a place to share your love for your angel. If you choose, you can continue to have a relationship with your loved one even though they are not physically here. This process will help you continue to speak with them and share your love for them. It is also a place where you can record those special sacred dreams. It is speaking and journaling heart to heart.

Love your friend,

Jen

Heart to Heart   **Date:___/___/___.**

Dear _____,

_____

_____

_____

_____

_____

_____

_____

_____

_____

_____

_____

_____

_____

_____

_____

_____

_____

_____

_____

_____

_____

_____

_____

_____

Heart to Heart

_____

_____

_____

_____

_____

_____

_____

_____

_____

_____

_____

_____

_____

_____

_____

_____

_____

_____

_____

_____

_____

_____

_____

_____

_____

_____

Heart to Heart   **Date:___/___/___.**

If I had 5 minutes to ask you anything it would be _____

_____

_____

_____

_____

_____

_____

_____

_____

_____

                                                      Date:___/___/___.

If I could relive one memory with you it would be _____

_____

_____

_____

_____

_____

_____

_____

_____

_____

_____

_____

Heart to Heart

Date:____/____/____.

Heart to Heart   Date:___/___/___.

I felt so proud of you when _____

_____

_____

_____

_____

_____

_____

_____

_____

                                                Date:___/___/___.

If I got one day to spend with you it would be _____

_____

_____

_____

_____

_____

_____

_____

_____

_____

_____

_____

_____

_____

Heart to Heart

Date:___/___/___.

_____
_____
_____
_____
_____
_____
_____
_____
_____
_____
_____
_____
_____
_____
_____
_____
_____
_____
_____
_____
_____
_____
_____
_____
_____
_____

Heart to Heart   **Date:___/___/___.**

You have taught me _____

_____

_____

_____

_____

_____

_____

_____

_____

_____

_____

                                                      Date:___/___/___.

If I had to say goodbye all over again I would want you to know _____

_____

_____

_____

_____

_____

_____

_____

_____

_____

_____

_____

Heart to Heart

_____
_____
_____
_____
_____
_____
_____
_____
_____
_____
_____
_____
_____
_____
_____
_____
_____
_____
_____
_____
_____
_____
_____
_____
_____
_____
_____
_____
_____

Heart to Heart   **Date:___/___/___.**

The legacy I choose to live in your honor is_____

_____

_____

_____

_____

_____

_____

_____

_____

_____

                                                       Date:___/___/___.

My relationship with you now is _____

_____

_____

_____

_____

_____

_____

_____

_____

_____

_____

_____

_____

Heart to Heart

Heart to Heart   **Date:___/___/___.**

You have taught me_____

_____

_____

_____

_____

_____

_____

_____

_____

_____

_____

                                            Date:___/___/___.

You are the reason _____

_____

_____

_____

_____

_____

_____

_____

_____

_____

_____

_____

Heart to Heart

_____
_____
_____
_____
_____
_____
_____
_____
_____
_____
_____
_____
_____
_____
_____
_____
_____
_____
_____
_____
_____
_____
_____
_____
_____
_____

Heart to Heart   **Date:** ___ / ___ / ___ .

I dreamed of you last night _____

_____

_____

_____

_____

_____

_____

_____

_____

_____

_____

_____

_____

_____

_____

_____

_____

_____

_____

_____

_____

_____

_____

_____

_____

_____

Heart to Heart

Date:____/____/____.

_____
_____
_____
_____
_____
_____
_____
_____
_____
_____
_____
_____
_____
_____
_____
_____
_____
_____
_____
_____
_____
_____
_____
_____
_____
_____
_____

Heart to Heart   **Date:** ___ / ___ / ___ .

Heart to Heart

Date:___/___/___.

_____

_____

_____

_____

_____

_____

_____

_____

_____

_____

_____

_____

_____

_____

_____

_____

_____

_____

_____

_____

_____

_____

_____

_____

_____

_____

Heart to Heart

Heart to Heart   **Date:** ___ / ___ / ___ .

_____

_____

_____

_____

_____

_____

_____

_____

_____

_____

_____

_____

_____

_____

_____

_____

_____

_____

_____

_____

_____

_____

_____

_____

_____

_____

_____

_____

_____

Heart to Heart

Date:_____/_____/_____.

_____

_____

_____

_____

_____

_____

_____

_____

_____

_____

_____

_____

_____

_____

_____

_____

_____

_____

_____

_____

_____

_____

_____

_____

_____

_____

_____

Heart to Heart

Date:___/___/___.

Heart to Heart

Date:___/___/___.

_____
_____
_____
_____
_____
_____
_____
_____
_____
_____
_____
_____
_____
_____
_____
_____
_____
_____
_____
_____
_____
_____
_____
_____
_____
_____
_____
_____

Heart to Heart   **Date:** ___ / ___ / ___ .

_____
_____
_____
_____
_____
_____
_____
_____
_____
_____
_____
_____
_____
_____
_____
_____
_____
_____
_____
_____
_____
_____
_____
_____
_____
_____
_____
_____
_____

Heart to Heart

Heart to Heart   Date:___/___/___.

_____

_____

_____

_____

_____

_____

_____

_____

_____

_____

_____

_____

_____

_____

_____

_____

_____

_____

_____

_____

_____

_____

_____

_____

_____

_____

_____

_____

_____

Heart to Heart

_____
_____
_____
_____
_____
_____
_____
_____
_____
_____
_____
_____
_____
_____
_____
_____
_____
_____
_____
_____
_____
_____
_____
_____
_____
_____
_____
_____

Heart to Heart   Date:___/___/___.

_____
_____
_____
_____
_____
_____
_____
_____
_____
_____
_____
_____
_____
_____
_____
_____
_____
_____
_____
_____
_____
_____
_____
_____
_____
_____
_____
_____

Heart to Heart

_____

_____

_____

_____

_____

_____

_____

_____

_____

_____

_____

_____

_____

_____

_____

_____

_____

_____

_____

_____

_____

_____

_____

_____

_____

_____

_____

Where there is
HOPE,
There is
FAITH,
Where there is faith
MIRACLES
Happen.

———————— ♡ ♡ ♡ ————————

Be Still my Soul

"Hope is being able to see that there is light despite all of the darkness."

B e Still My Soul…be still, pray, listen, and then write. This section is full of blank pages for you to use the prompts at the beginning of the journal if you would like or to freely write whatever is in your heart and mind. This is a SACRED record because it is YOURS. It's your journey through grief. Let all of it out: the good, the bad, and the ugly. Let this be the moment that you can be true and authentic to your thoughts and feelings. No judgements here, just pure and true grieving, whatever that may look like today. Let that weight pressing on your chest slowly be lifted as you write. I know as you do so, little by little your heart will begin to piece back together.

As time goes on and you come back to this and read through your journey, you will be able to see how miraculous and strong you are, even though right now you probably don't feel that way. You will be able to see more clearly the Savior working in your life. You will notice where you saw that glimpse of hope in the darkness, and you reached out and grabbed it.

You, my friend, have taken another step forward.

Continue to have HOPE, receive HOPE, and give HOPE whenever you can. I know as you do so, your heart will slowly begin to mend, and a beautiful legacy will be created.

This is my prayer for you!

Love your friend,

Jen

Be Still my Soul

Date:____/____/____.

Be Still my Soul

Date:___/___/___.

Be Still my Soul

Date:___/___/___.

_____

_____

_____

_____

_____

_____

_____

_____

_____

_____

_____

_____

_____

_____

_____

_____

_____

_____

_____

_____

_____

_____

_____

_____

Be Still my Soul   **Date:___/___/___.**

_____

_____

_____

_____

_____

_____

_____

_____

_____

_____

_____

_____

_____

_____

_____

_____

_____

_____

_____

_____

_____

_____

_____

_____

_____

_____

_____

_____

_____

Be Still my Soul

Date:____/____/____.

_____

_____

_____

_____

_____

_____

_____

_____

_____

_____

_____

_____

_____

_____

_____

_____

_____

_____

_____

_____

_____

_____

_____

_____

_____

_____

_____

Be Still my Soul   Date:____/____/____.

_____

_____

_____

_____

_____

_____

_____

_____

_____

_____

_____

_____

_____

_____

_____

_____

_____

_____

_____

_____

_____

_____

_____

_____

_____

_____

_____

Be Still my Soul

_____

_____

_____

_____

_____

_____

_____

_____

_____

_____

_____

_____

_____

_____

_____

_____

_____

_____

_____

_____

_____

_____

_____

_____

_____

Be Still my Soul

_____

_____

_____

_____

_____

_____

_____

_____

_____

_____

_____

_____

_____

_____

_____

_____

_____

_____

_____

_____

_____

_____

_____

_____

_____

_____

_____

_____

_____

_____

Be Still my Soul   Date:___/___/___.

_____

_____

_____

_____

_____

_____

_____

_____

_____

_____

_____

_____

_____

_____

_____

_____

_____

_____

_____

_____

_____

_____

_____

_____

_____

Be Still my Soul

Be Still my Soul

_____

_____

_____

_____

_____

_____

_____

_____

_____

_____

_____

_____

_____

_____

_____

_____

_____

_____

_____

_____

_____

_____

_____

_____

_____

_____

Be Still my Soul

_____

_____

_____

_____

_____

_____

_____

_____

_____

_____

_____

_____

_____

_____

_____

_____

_____

_____

_____

_____

_____

_____

_____

_____

_____

_____

_____

_____

Be Still my Soul

_____
_____
_____
_____
_____
_____
_____
_____
_____
_____
_____
_____
_____
_____
_____
_____
_____
_____
_____
_____
_____
_____
_____
_____
_____
_____
_____
_____
_____

Be Still my Soul

Date:____/____/____.

_____

_____

_____

_____

_____

_____

_____

_____

_____

_____

_____

_____

_____

_____

_____

_____

_____

_____

_____

_____

_____

_____

_____

_____

_____

_____

_____

_____

Be Still my Soul

_____

_____

_____

_____

_____

_____

_____

_____

_____

_____

_____

_____

_____

_____

_____

_____

_____

_____

_____

_____

_____

_____

_____

_____

Be Still my Soul   Date:___/___/____.

_____

_____

_____

_____

_____

_____

_____

_____

_____

_____

_____

_____

_____

_____

_____

_____

_____

_____

_____

_____

_____

_____

_____

_____

_____

_____

_____

_____

Be Still my Soul   Date:___/___/___.

_____
_____
_____
_____
_____
_____
_____
_____
_____
_____
_____
_____
_____
_____
_____
_____
_____
_____
_____
_____
_____
_____
_____
_____
_____
_____
_____

Be Still my Soul   Date:___/___/___.

_____
_____
_____
_____
_____
_____
_____
_____
_____
_____
_____
_____
_____
_____
_____
_____
_____
_____
_____
_____
_____
_____
_____
_____
_____

Be Still my Soul

Be Still my Soul   Date:___ / ___ / ___ .

Be Still my Soul

Date:____/____/____.

Be Still my Soul Date:___/___/___.

Be Still my Soul Date:___/___/___.

_____
_____
_____
_____
_____
_____
_____
_____
_____
_____
_____
_____
_____
_____
_____
_____
_____
_____
_____
_____
_____
_____
_____
_____
_____
_____

Be Still my Soul

Be Still my Soul

Date:____/____/____.

Be Still my Soul

Date:___/___/___.

Be Still my Soul

_____

_____

_____

_____

_____

_____

_____

_____

_____

_____

_____

_____

_____

_____

_____

_____

_____

_____

_____

_____

_____

_____

_____

_____

_____

_____

_____

_____

_____

_____

Be Still my Soul   **Date:** ___ / ___ / ___ .

_____
_____
_____
_____
_____
_____
_____
_____
_____
_____
_____
_____
_____
_____
_____
_____
_____
_____
_____
_____
_____
_____
_____
_____
_____
_____
_____
_____

Be Still my Soul

_____

_____

_____

_____

_____

_____

_____

_____

_____

_____

_____

_____

_____

_____

_____

_____

_____

_____

_____

_____

_____

_____

_____

_____

_____

_____

Be Still my Soul

Be Still my Soul

_____

_____

_____

_____

_____

_____

_____

_____

_____

_____

_____

_____

_____

_____

_____

_____

_____

_____

_____

_____

_____

_____

_____

_____

_____

_____

Be Still my Soul   Date:____/____/____.

_____

_____

_____

_____

_____

_____

_____

_____

_____

_____

_____

_____

_____

_____

_____

_____

_____

_____

_____

_____

_____

_____

_____

_____

_____

_____

_____

_____

Be Still my Soul

_____

_____

_____

_____

_____

_____

_____

_____

_____

_____

_____

_____

_____

_____

_____

_____

_____

_____

_____

_____

_____

_____

_____

_____

_____

Be Still my Soul   Date:___/___/___.

Be Still my Soul

_____

_____

_____

_____

_____

_____

_____

_____

_____

_____

_____

_____

_____

_____

_____

_____

_____

_____

_____

_____

_____

_____

_____

_____

_____

_____

Be Still my Soul   Date:____/____/____.

_____

_____

_____

_____

_____

_____

_____

_____

_____

_____

_____

_____

_____

_____

_____

_____

_____

_____

_____

_____

_____

_____

_____

_____

_____

_____

_____

_____

_____

Be Still my Soul

_____

_____

_____

_____

_____

_____

_____

_____

_____

_____

_____

_____

_____

_____

_____

_____

_____

_____

_____

_____

_____

_____

_____

_____

_____

_____

Be Still my Soul   Date:____/____/____.

_____

_____

_____

_____

_____

_____

_____

_____

_____

_____

_____

_____

_____

_____

_____

_____

_____

_____

_____

_____

_____

_____

_____

_____

_____

_____

Be Still my Soul

Be Still my Soul

Be Still my Soul　　　　　　　**Date:___/___/___.**

_____
_____
_____
_____
_____
_____
_____
_____
_____
_____
_____
_____
_____
_____
_____
_____
_____
_____
_____
_____
_____
_____
_____
_____

Be Still my Soul　　　　　　　　　　　　　Date:___/___/___.

Be Still my Soul

_____

_____

_____

_____

_____

_____

_____

_____

_____

_____

_____

_____

_____

_____

_____

_____

_____

_____

_____

_____

_____

_____

_____

_____

_____

Be Still my Soul

Date:___/___/___.

Be Still my Soul

Date:___/___/___.

_____
_____
_____
_____
_____
_____
_____
_____
_____
_____
_____
_____
_____
_____
_____
_____
_____
_____
_____
_____
_____
_____
_____
_____
_____
_____

Be Still my Soul

Be Still my Soul

_____
_____
_____
_____
_____
_____
_____
_____
_____
_____
_____
_____
_____
_____
_____
_____
_____
_____
_____
_____
_____
_____
_____
_____
_____
_____

Be Still my Soul

Date:___/___/___.

Be Still my Soul

Date:____/____/____.

I will learn to live in the
sunshine of your life
instead of the
dark shadow of your death.

———————— ♡ ♡ ♡ ————————

Thoughts and Feelings

"Owning our Story and Loving ourselves through
that process is the Bravest thing we'll ever do."
~Brene Brown

Dear Friend,

We have come so far in this journal. I hope you have found hope in your writing of memories, feelings and grief. This last section is a bonus exercise for you. I include this section because I didn't understand this concept for the first few years of my grieving process with my first daughter.

When we are in grief, we have so many thoughts and feelings surrounding the passing of our loved one. This short exercise will bring awareness to how you are thinking and how those thoughts are making you feel. Most of us are unaware of the power that our thoughts really have, especially in grief. We often have thoughts that create sad feelings and rightfully so. However, sometimes our thoughts can create suffering in our sadness.

Did you know that you don't have to suffer in your grief? After the loss of my first daughter, I didn't know that. I equated the length of my suffering to the amount of love I had for her. One day, I had a light bulb moment when I heard someone say, "What do you want your daughter's legacy to be?" It finally clicked for me. I didn't want her memory to be one of pain, sadness, and suffering. I want my daughter's legacy to be one of light, love, and happiness. In that moment, I knew that the measure of my love wasn't conditioned on how long I was miserable in the pain of her loss.

This didn't mean I didn't have days that still brought me to my knees. It didn't even make the loss okay. What it did do was bring some added peace and meaning to the loss. Along with my Savior's help, I could keep taking steps forward, bringing the loss with me, but also creating a life of joy for myself and my family, all in honor of my daughter and now daughters.

Here is how you can use this Bonus section:

1. Start by writing down the main thought you are having. *No judgments of the thought, just write it down.*

2. Then close your eyes and place your hand over your heart and say that thought out loud.

3. When you say it out loud, recognize how that thought makes you feel. Sometimes it will create sadness, anger, anxiety. Other times it may create happiness, joy, and at times relief. *No judgments here either. Just write down the feeling.*

4. Finally, write what is coming up for you. Ask yourself, what am I thinking?

5. Once you fill out the section, go back and ask yourself a few of these questions: What are you aware of that you didn't notice before? Is this a thought and feeling you want right now? Is it something you need to feel?

Becoming aware of our thoughts and feelings helps us process our grief. Allowing our emotions to come and recognizing them is essential to our healing and growth in life. It also allows us to decide what thought and feeling serve us and what doesn't. Once we do so, a whole new world opens up for us and we bring our loved one's legacy with us and through us.

I hope you consider this section a gift from me to you. I am praying for you!

Love your friend,

Jen

Thoughts and Feelings   Date:____/____/____.

Thought:_____

_____

Feeling: _____

_____

What's coming up for you? _____

_____

_____

_____

_____

Thoughts and Feelings   Date:____/____/____.

Thought:_____

_____

Feeling: _____

_____

What's coming up for you? _____

_____

_____

_____

_____

Thoughts and Feelings   Date:___/___/___.

Thought:_____

_____

_____

Feeling: _____

_____

_____

What's coming up for you? _____

_____

_____

_____

Thoughts and Feelings   Date:___/___/___.

Thought:_____

_____

_____

Feeling: _____

_____

_____

What's coming up for you?_____

_____

_____

_____

_____

Thoughts and Feelings   **Date:___/___/___.**

Thought:_____

_____

Feeling: _____

_____

What's coming up for you? _____

_____

_____

_____

_____

Thoughts and Feelings   **Date:___/___/___.**

Thought:_____

_____

Feeling: _____

_____

What's coming up for you? _____

_____

_____

_____

_____

Thoughts and Feelings   **Date:___/___/____.**

Thought:_____

_____

_____

Feeling: _____

_____

_____

What's coming up for you? _____

_____

_____

_____

Thoughts and Feelings   **Date:___/___/____.**

Thought:_____

_____

_____

Feeling: _____

_____

_____

What's coming up for you?_____

_____

_____

_____

_____

Thoughts and Feelings   Date:___/___/___.

Thought:_____

_____

Feeling: _____

_____

What's coming up for you? _____

_____

_____

_____

_____

Thoughts and Feelings   Date:___/___/___.

Thought:_____

_____

Feeling: _____

_____

What's coming up for you? _____

_____

_____

_____

_____

_____

Thoughts and Feelings   Date:___/___/___.

Thought:_____

_____

_____

Feeling: _____

_____

_____

What's coming up for you? _____

_____

_____

_____

Thoughts and Feelings   Date:___/___/___.

Thought:_____

_____

_____

Feeling: _____

_____

_____

What's coming up for you?_____

_____

_____

_____

_____

Thoughts and Feelings   **Date:___/___/___.**

Thought:_____

_____

Feeling: _____

_____

What's coming up for you? _____

_____

_____

_____

_____

Thoughts and Feelings   **Date:___/___/___.**

Thought:_____

_____

Feeling: _____

_____

What's coming up for you? _____

_____

_____

_____

_____

_____

_____

Thoughts and Feelings   **Date:___/___/___.**

Thought:_____

_____

_____

Feeling: _____

_____

_____

What's coming up for you? _____

_____

_____

_____

Thoughts and Feelings   **Date:___/___/___.**

Thought:_____

_____

_____

Feeling: _____

_____

_____

What's coming up for you?_____

_____

_____

_____

_____

Thoughts and Feelings   Date:____/____/____.

Thought:_____

_____

Feeling: _____

_____

What's coming up for you? _____

_____

_____

_____

_____

Thoughts and Feelings   Date:____/____/____.

Thought:_____

_____

Feeling: _____

_____

What's coming up for you? _____

_____

_____

_____

_____

Thoughts and Feelings Date:___/___/___.

Thought:_____

_____

_____

Feeling: _____

_____

_____

What's coming up for you? _____

_____

_____

_____

Thoughts and Feelings Date:___/___/___.

Thought:_____

_____

_____

Feeling: _____

_____

_____

What's coming up for you?_____

_____

_____

_____

_____

Thoughts and Feelings   **Date:___/___/____.**

Thought:_____

_____

Feeling: _____

_____

What's coming up for you? _____

_____

_____

_____

_____

Thoughts and Feelings   **Date:___/___/____.**

Thought:_____

_____

Feeling: _____

_____

What's coming up for you? _____

_____

_____

_____

_____

_____

Thoughts and Feelings   **Date:____/____/____.**

Thought:_____

_____

_____

Feeling: _____

_____

_____

What's coming up for you? _____

_____

_____

_____

Thoughts and Feelings   **Date:____/____/____.**

Thought:_____

_____

_____

Feeling: _____

_____

_____

What's coming up for you?_____

_____

_____

_____

Thoughts and Feelings   **Date:** ___/___/___ .

Thought:_____

_____

Feeling: _____

_____

What's coming up for you? _____

_____

_____

_____

Thoughts and Feelings   **Date:** ___/___/___ .

Thought:_____

_____

Feeling: _____

_____

What's coming up for you? _____

_____

_____

_____

Thoughts and Feelings   **Date:**___/___/___.

Thought:_____

_____

_____

Feeling: _____

_____

_____

What's coming up for you? _____

_____

_____

_____

Thoughts and Feelings   **Date:**___/___/___.

Thought:_____

_____

_____

Feeling: _____

_____

_____

What's coming up for you?_____

_____

_____

_____

_____

Thoughts and Feelings   **Date:___/___/___.**

Thought:_____

_____

Feeling: _____

_____

What's coming up for you? _____

_____

_____

_____

_____

Thoughts and Feelings   **Date:___/___/___.**

Thought:_____

_____

Feeling: _____

_____

What's coming up for you? _____

_____

_____

_____

_____

_____

Thoughts and Feelings Date:____/____/____.

Thought:_____

_____

_____

Feeling: _____

_____

_____

What's coming up for you? _____

_____

_____

_____

Thoughts and Feelings Date:____/____/____.

Thought:_____

_____

_____

Feeling: _____

_____

_____

What's coming up for you?_____

_____

_____

_____

_____

Thoughts and Feelings   **Date:___/___/___.**

Thought:_____

_____

Feeling: _____

_____

What's coming up for you? _____

_____

_____

_____

_____

Thoughts and Feelings   **Date:___/___/___.**

Thought:_____

_____

Feeling: _____

_____

What's coming up for you? _____

_____

_____

_____

_____

May love be
what you remember
most.

———————— ♡ ♡ ♡ ————————

-Darcie Sims

Made in the USA
Las Vegas, NV
10 July 2022

51343299R00116